WATERCOLOURS
THE CHARLES LEES COLLECTION
AT OLDHAM ART GALLERY

TREVOR COOMBS

CONTENTS

First published in Great Britain in 1993 by Oldham Art Gallery, Union Street, Oldham OL1 1DN

A CIP catalogue record for this book is available from the British Library

ISBN 0-902-80925-3

Printed and bound in England by Belmont Press Ltd

Cover: John Varley, *Glengary Loch*

PREFACE

The Charles Lees Collection of British Watercolours, presented in 1888, remains the single most important gift to Oldham Art Gallery. Individual paintings from the collection have been displayed frequently both in Oldham and in numerous galleries throughout Britain and abroad. But it is many years since the Charles Lees Collection has been seen in its entirety.

Watercolours are, by the very nature of the media used in their making, fragile and extremely vulnerable to light, and a century of exhibitions had taken its its toll on the Lees Collection – by 1987 many works were faded and dilapidated. A five year conservation programme commenced that year to restore the paintings. It was carried out by North West Museums Service. Conservation was funded by Oldham Council with generous assistance from The Pilgrim Trust, Shell UK, and The Turner Society.

This publication celebrates the restoration and redisplay of the collection. Written and researched by Trevor Coombs, former Keeper of Art at Oldham, it places Charles Lees and his collection in social and historical context. It catalogues the collection in detail, concentrating on the main part of the gift – 80 watercolours presented in 1888. In keeping with Charles Lees' intention, and in the spirit of Edward Abbott Parry's original catalogue of 1889, these works are catalogued chronologically by artist. These works make up the bulk of the catalogue, along with the Liber Studiorum of Turner and other fine art works collected by Lees and presented to Oldham Art Gallery at other times prior to his death or, subsequently, by his daughter, Marjory Lees. An additional essay focusing on key paintings was written by Michael Clarke, Keeper of Paintings (National Gallery of Scotland). We thank both Trevor Coombs and Michael Clarke.

Our warm thanks also to Blair French for exemplary editing, to Tessa Gudgeon, Senior Art Gallery Officer, to the Paul Mellon Centre, the Granada Foundation, and, of course, to Tina Vaughan and Sean Moore of Dorling Kindersley for their invaluable work on the production of this publication.

Aileen McEvoy
Principal Museum and Gallery Officer
Oldham Art Gallery, 1993

CHARLES LEES AND ART PATRONAGE IN THE NINETEENTH CENTURY

Charles E. Lees (1840-1894)
Lees' gift to the gallery of 80
watercolours was meant to
introduce the people of
Oldham to watercolour
painting.

The Charles Lees Collection of British Watercolours is a fine example of one highly respected nineteenth-century collector's perspective on British watercolour painting. Containing works by the finest British watercolourists, it is significant not only aesthetically and art historically, but also in wider social contexts.

Prominent Oldham industrialist Charles E. Lees was involved in the establishment of Oldham Art Gallery in 1883, loaning works from his own collection for exhibitions and convincing others to do likewise; he also sat on the first Gallery committees. As well as this, Lees was a member of the Fine Arts Section of the 1887 Royal Jubilee Committee, and, in 1889, was a founder governor of the Manchester Whitworth Institute (now Whitworth Art Gallery) to which he donated 13 watercolours.

In 1888 Charles Lees made a gift to Oldham Art Gallery of 80 watercolour paintings and drawings from his private collection. This gift was intended to introduce Oldham people to British watercolour painting. It remains the single most significant acquisition in the history of Oldham Art Gallery.

THE LIFE OF CHARLES LEES

The development of Charles Lees' private art collection and his gift to Oldham Art Gallery illustrates the changing role of art patronage amongst the prospering middle classes in Britain during the nineteenth century. The emergent social concerns of nineteenth-century reformism led to a new type of private art collector and the establishment of many of the public art institutions that still exist today. Their newly acquired role of art benefactor gave the middle classes some control over the limited leisure time of the working classes. No matter how benevolent in intent, this served to reinforce power relationships in Victorian Society. Serving up cultural enlightenment in the form of fine art also served to salve the consciences of industrialists whose operations and profit motives condemned the working classes to a difficult, deprived and often dangerous life, in addition to harming the local environment.

The Charles Lees Collection is one private collector's personal study of British watercolour painting, but it also indicates some of the moral attitudes of nineteenth-century middle-class art patrons. Charles Lees was born into an already highly successful family of Oldham industrialists. His grandfather – Samuel Lees – established an iron foundry in Oldham in 1816. This business expanded hugely over the next 30 years with Samuel Lees acquiring great personal wealth. On Samuel Lees' death the business was split between his three sons – Eli, Asa and Job. Businesswise Charles' father Eli was the most successful of the three. In 1846 he launched into cotton spinning and weaving, making the bulk of his wealth from the cotton boom. By 1866 Oldham had more cotton spindles than any other town in the world.

A PRIVILEDGED LIFE

Charles Lees began working in the family business in the late 1850s, taking it over during the late 1870s/early 1880s as Samuel Lees gradually withdrew from business activity. By this time the success of the business was ensured, its great expansionist drive essentially complete. This is significant as, although considered a highly successful businessman, Charles Lees needed to manage rather than expand the family business, leaving him time and energy to pursue his interests and commitments in religion and the arts. The family wealth was also significant in that it allowed Charles Lees to grow up with an education in Paris and Hanover, surrounded by fine art, furniture, and objects, and with overseas holidays. On his marriage to Sarah Anne Buckley in 1874 he was given the family house in what is now Werneth Park – a property bought by Eli Lees along with three other local industrialists in 1847. Throughout his life Charles Lees was surrounded by wealth, comfortable with the exposure to high culture that it brought.

The continued development of the Lees family through successive generations encapsulates the great social change that took place in nineteenth-century Britain; the shifting of political, economic and cultural power from the aristocracy to the growing middle classes. The Great Reform Act of 1832 brought about a new political franchise based on property, which shifted political power towards the new middle classes. Although it only increased the voting population from 10% to 15% of adult males, it did initiate a form of representative democracy based around the Tory and Liberal parties. A second act in 1867 gave 33% of adult males the right to vote, making it necessary for political parties to canvas wider political support for the first time. Charles Lees grew up in a liberal environment, surrounded in particular by the ideas and morality of liberal reformism.

Samuel Lees (1773-1845)
Charles Lees' grandfather, who established the successful family manufacturing business.

This was an attitude of social concern, a commitment to social improvement, an outlook of caring capitalism that was prevalent amongst a significant section of the middle classes. Charles Lees was very much a product of liberal reformism, committed to the improvement of living conditions for the working classes and to enlightenment for everyone through exposure to culture and the arts. Reformism, however, also served the new social power structures. Power newly acquired by the middle classes was fiercely protected, not to be easily relinquished or even shared. The fear of mob rule was very real, reinforced by the Chartist riots of the 1840's. Reformism was also a means of encouraging social harmony; 'civilising', keeping the masses happy, was a

Eli Lees (1815-1892)
Charles Lees' father, who moved into spinning and weaving, creating even greater wealth for the Lees family.

Dame Sarah-Anne Lees
née Buckley (1842-1935)
Married Charles Lees in 1874.
After his death she became a
Liberal town councillor and
Oldham's first woman mayor.
She was also heavily involved
in the Suffrage movement.

Marjory Lees (1878-1970)
Second daughter of Charles
and Sarah - also a councillor.

means of defusing social conflict and entrenching the status quo: the power of the middles classes. For many, this was an explicit aim of reformism. For example, educational organizations such as Working Men's Colleges or the Mechanics Institutes were established to promote harmony through access to education, as well as to improve worker productivity.

SOCIAL IDEALS

Whilst politics was the most obvious vehicle for pursuing social ideals, Charles Lees did not directly involve himself politically, despite being friends with Liberal M.P. for Oldham, Sir John Hibbert. In fact he appears to have deliberately avoided public life, apart from a short period as a magistrate from 1889. It was his wife, Sarah Anne, who moved into politics after Charles' death in 1894. She became a Liberal councillor in 1907 and later the first woman mayor of Oldham, one of the first in the country. Along with her daughter Marjory, who also became a town councillor, Sarah Anne Lees was heavily involved in the Women's Suffrage movement during the early part of this century.

Charles Lees preferred to further his social ideals through religion and the arts. The Lees family were religious non-conformists, part of the early-nineteenth-century evangelical movement that campaigned passionately for such things as education and the improvement of social conditions. Samuel Lees had financially supported the establishment of Hope church in 1824, and his grandson Charles continued this spiritual and practical commitment.

As in other spheres of life, the shift of power in the nineteenth century from the aristocracy to the middle classes challenged old standards and assumptions of taste in art. With new wealth came opportunities for art collecting, and the acquisition of art was a method of signifying status and indicating power. The shift of art patronage from the aristocracy to middle classes influenced a change in artistic themes through the 1840s and 1850s. Aristocratic taste for Old Masters was superseded by a demand for work by contemporary British artists. Collectors wanted artworks reflecting their own lives, aspirations and moral concerns, so landscapes and domestic scenes prevailed – works with an obvious moralistic and religious content, emphasising Victorian ideals such as hard work.

Patronage took on a new style with the down-to-earth approach of the new collectors who were careful how they spent their wealth. Work by living artists was cheaper than Old Masters, and collectors used to having control over production in their business lives came into direct contact with artists, overseeing their own commissions. Art was involved in a dynamic relationship with other agents of social and political change during the nineteenth century, both informing change and being shaped by it.

Charles Lees bought his first works of art in the 1860s, rather traditional works with literary and academic themes. By the 1870s, however, his maturity in outlook was reflected in his art collecting activity. Sure of his business future and of his social position, his collecting reflected both his love of watercolour and a confidence in his own aesthetic sense that had been encouraged by his friendship with William and George Agnew. The Agnew family had set up as art dealers in Manchester in 1817, opening offices in Liverpool in 1859 and in London in 1860. By the 1870s they were one of the most important art dealerships in Britain. Charles Lees had been introduced to the Agnew family by his father Eli in the early 1870s and the strong friendship that ensued was a major factor in Charles Lees' development as an art collector.

ASSESSING THE COLLECTION

Whilst the idea of attempting an overview of the history of British watercolour painting certainly guided Charles Lees' collecting practice, it does not seem to have been an obsessive principle in his selection of work. He was, in any case, necessarily restricted by what was available. The process of selecting a group of works for Oldham Art Gallery from the 300 or so watercolours in his collection in 1887 would have enabled Lees to summarise his collection, assess its strengths and weaknesses, and would have provided him with a focus for further acquisitions. Indeed, between 1888 and 1894 Charles Lees acquired some of his finest works.

Charles Lees' does not appear to have been motivated by investment or public status concerns in the development of his collection; very few works were ever sold and he shied away from public displays of gratitude for his gift to Oldham Art Gallery. Rather, the gift seems to have been motivated by social ideals, particularly educational ones. Charles Lees was involved with and supported Oldham Art Gallery right from its inception. The gallery was initially concerned with establishing itself with large exhibitions such as the Annual Spring Exhibition following the style of Royal Academy exhibitions. Educational functions were not an initial priority. The Lees gift was presented as educational, shaped and defined as a survey of British watercolours with Charles Lees own strongly stated desire that it should be on display and accessible to as large a section of the public for as long as possible. (He campaigned vigorously for free admission and weekend opening hours outside of standard working hours.) A catalogue detailing the collection and providing information about artists represented in it was commissioned from art critic Edward Abbott Parry and was published in 1889.

The history of the Lees family through the nineteenth and into the twentieth century is quite remarkable. From Samuel Lees' industrialist drive through to Sarah Anne and Marjory Lees' pioneering political activities, the family's development epitomises the rise of the middle classes in nineteenth century Britain, with the concurrent shifts in power structures and moral attitudes. Charles Lees' activities as an art collector, patron and benefactor similarly epitomise the social functions of art in Victorian Britain; its use in the pursuit of social ideals in the hands of reformist liberals promoting aesthetic pleasure and knowledge, alongside its role in reinforcing the new power and status of the middle classes. Ultimately, whatever Charles Lees' awareness of and attitude to the wider social implications of his role as a public benefactor, he did genuinely contribute something significant, to the Oldham community in which he lived in the form of this superb collection of watercolours.

Blair French

NOTE
The research for this introductory essay was carried out by Trevor Coombs. This introduction is based upon more detailed essays written by Trevor Coombs regarding Charles Lees and the Charles Lees Collection of Watercolours. These essays are available from Oldham Art Gallery and Oldham Local Studies Library.

AN INTRODUCTION TO WATERCOLOURS

Charles Lees' concern "to show the rise and progress" of watercolour painting was one that was shared by other nineteenth-century collectors and commentators. In 1824 the artist William Henry Pyne (1769-1845) had entitles a series of articles "The Rise and Progress of watercolour painting in England". The period he described was very much that covered by the earlier half of the Lees collection, from the topographical watercolours of Paul Sandby (*Old House with Figures*) in the mid-eighteenth century, then perceived to be mere tinted drawings, to the paintings in watercolour of Thomas Girtin and J.M.W. Turner. The distinction is significant, for watercolour was considered, in just over a half a century, to have develped from being little more than a mainly utilitarian medium suitable for the depiction of "abbeys, castle, ancient towns and noblemen's seats" to one capable of embodying greater concepts such as the grandeur of nature.

At the time that Pyne wrote his articles Turner was held, quite rightly, to one of the greatest, if least understood, of all British artists. There were regular exhibitions of watercolours in London, and a whole host of young men and, more particularly, ladies were instructed in the genteel art of watercolour painting. Watercolour's enormous success was a peculiarly British phenomenon, observed as such by commentators on the Continent and, through the agency of artists such as Bonington (*Le Tréport seen from the Direction of Eu*), it was enormously influential on a whole genera-

tion of French landscape painters. As the nineteenth century unfolded an increasing number of collectors turned to watercolours, which were available in profusion. The wealthy and the comfortably off could afford to buy them. If the eighteenth century had been the great era of the landed gentry embellishing their country houses with Old Master paintings and classical statuary, then in the nineteenth it was the turn of the nouveau riche industrialists to fill their suburban villas with watercolours of the British School. As the critic John Ruskin wrote in 1880, "The great people always bought Canaletto, not Prout (*The Rialto*), and Van Huysum, not Hunt (*An Interior*). There was indeed no quality in the bright little watercolours, which indeed could look other than pert in ghostly corridors, and petty in halls of state; but they gave an unquestionable tone of liberal-mindeness to a suburban villa, and were the cheerfullest-possible decorations for a moderate-sized breakfast parlour, opening on a nicely-mowed lawn."

All too frequently, however, these watercolous were placed in the full glare of the sun, the light streaming in through the drawing-room windows. Watercolours were also displayed in museums and there too they received injurious amounts of light. The relatively delicate medium failed to prevent the colours, formed by particles of pigment, from fading in strong light. Paradoxical though it may seem, many nineteenth-century enthusiasts for watercolours contributed to their partial destruction through excessive zeal and an ignorance of the physical properties of the medium. Today, by contrast, watercolours are carefully stored in special boxes and only exhibited for limited periods of time under strictly controlled lighting.

Technically speaking, "Watercolour" denotes any type of paint that can be mixed in water. Water is used to spread the paint onto the painting surface and then, its job done, it evaporates. The particles of colour, the pigments, are stuck to the painting surface by a binder, essentially a glue. This is usually made of gum arabic, a substance obtained from the acacia tree. "Traditional" watercolour normally produces transparent washes of colour through which the white of the paper surface is reflected. A typical example is Edward Dayes' view of Chepstow. Opaque white can be added, and this type of watercolour is called gouache or bod colour. In the nineteenth century, when watercolours tried to rival oils for brilliancy of colour and effect, bodycolour was increasingly used by artists like James Holland in his charming 1839 view of Venice. Later in the century there was a call for a return to the purity" of transparent watercolour.

Early watercolourists of the seventeenth century had to manufacture their own paints, purchasing the necessary ingredients from the apothecary's shop. By the later eighteenth century cakes of watercolour were being commercially manufactured by a number of firms amongst whom the pioneers were Reeves. These cakes could dry and crumble, therefore "moist" colours were subsequently developed whereby honey or glycerine were added to prevent the colours drying out. The nineteenth century also saw the introduction of tubes of watercolours, though these were rather frowned upon by purists.

The painting surface for watercolours has, of course, usually been paper, though in medieval times parchment had been used. Paper was introduced into Britain by a German, Sir John Spielman, in 1588. Traditionally, paper was made from the pulp of white linen and cotton rags. Boiled, washed and bleached, it was laid onto wire moulds, pressed into thin sheets and then hung up to dry. It was also dipped in glue or "size" to make it non-porous. It could then be painted on without the paper absorbing the watercolour to an excessive degree. Early paper was of very fine quality and was hand-made. In the nineteenth century poorer quality machine-made paper was also introduced.

Brushes were particularly important. Those of the finest quality were traditionally made from the hair of the red sable, a small animal of the marten family. Cheaper brushes were made from camel's hair. Very often the best brushes were quite large but, when wet, came to a very fine point, enabling even the most delicate work to be undertaken.

As the watercolourist's equipment became more sophisticated so did the containers in which it was stored or carried. Fashionable ladies, "colouring-in in their drawing-rooms", might have porcelain painting boxes manufactured by Wedgwood, while artists who travelled around Britain or abroad required tougher, portable boxes, usually made out wood, became very popular – an indication of the growing popularity of watercolours.

Technical advances were made in response to market needs. Watercolours were cheap, portable and relatively simple to use. They provided the perfect medium for the travelling artist and their popularity spread, particularly in the second half of the eighteenth century when a number of important social and cultural factors came into play. The fashion developed for touring hitherto disregarded parts of Britain such as the Lakes, Snowdonia and the Scottish Highlands. Edmund Burke's *Philosophical Enquiry into the*

Origin of our Ideas of the Sublime and the Beautiful was published in 1757. In it the Irish statesman and philosopher explained the ability of mountainous, "sublime" scenery to inspire fear and awe in the viewer; in other words to provide an aesthetic thrill. Coupled with this pursuit of new sensations was an increasing interest in the history and antiquities of the British Isles and nestling in the valleys, were the remains of the abbeys and monasteries that had escaped the Dissolution of the sixteenth century. The eighteenth century also saw a dramatic improvement in Britain's road systems. Travel became easier, whether it was to the native mountains, historical sites, the county race week or any of the great country houses and parks that were built at the time.

The subject-matter of eighteenth-century watercolours very much reflected these preoccupations, as a member of the Lees watercolours show – for example Thomas Hearne's little view of the beautiful ruins of Fountains Abbey in Yorkshire. A grander, more poetic view of nature, again featuring ruins but this time of the Greek temples of Paestum in southern Italy, is evinced in a magnificent watercolour by John Robert Cozens, perhaps the greatest genius of the art in the later eighteenth century. Cozens's grand, imaginative compositions were taken as a model by the generation of watercolourists who succeeded him at the beginning of the nineteenth century including Girtin and Turner. Girtin's *Egglestone Abbey*, another Yorkshire scene, represents a more ambitiously composed and fully coloured varia-tion on the theme of ecclesiastical ruins.

With the establishment in London of the Society of Painters in Watercolours in 1804 (further rival societies followed) water-colourists had regular venues at which to show their works. Although landscape predominated in the works of exhibitors such as John Varley, Peter De Wint and G.F. Robson, artists also depict-ed historical, mythological and genre scenes. One of the most enter-prising in this respect was Robert Hills who specialised in farmyard pictures but is represented in the Lees collection by a landscape *Turnip Field*.

Lees was admirably wide-ranging in his choice of pictures for his collection which ranges from the topography of the eighteenth cen-tury to the later Victorian hyper-realism of artists such as John William North whose finely detailed *Quantock Hills* is dated 1879. In his collecting habits Lees, like so many of his contemporaries, undoubtedly followed the advice contained in writings of his con-temporaries, undoubtedly followed the advice contained in the writings of John Ruskin, most particularly his *Modern Painters* which appeared in five volumes between 1843 and 1860 and functioned almost as a handbook for collectors. Such investment made good financial as well as artistic sense as the art dealer William Agnew confided in 1881, not to Lees, but to another of his clients, Samuel Ashton, "If I put my savings thirty years ago in good Watercolours .... I should be a rich man at this moment!" It was Oldham's good fortune that, in a spirit of Victorian philanthrop-ism, Lees made his presentation in 1888.

Michael Clarke
Keeper of Paintings, National Gallery of Scotland

THE

CHARLES LEES

COLLECTION

OF WATERCOLOURS

This section of the catalogue details the major section of the Charles
Lees Collection; 80 watercolours and drawings presented to Oldham Art
Gallery by Charles Lees in 1888. Works are listed chronologically by
artists' dates of birth.

Paul Sandby

Paul Sandby :
1725 - 1809

Paul Sandby was one of the most important topographical watercolour painters of the 18th century. He trained as a draughtsman at the Tower of London, and was later employed to survey regions of the Scottish Highlands. In addition to producing plans and maps, he spent a lot of spare time sketching outdoors. Though topographical, Sandby's watercolours illustrate an interest in the romantic aspects of nature, and in ideals of beauty.

Thomas Hearne :
1744 - 1817

Thomas Hearne trained as an engraver, but later turned towards producing topographical watercolours and drawings for other engravers to work from. He was a draughtsman to the Governer of the Leeward Islands in the West Indies for almost five years. Later, after returning to England in 1777, he began producing drawings for William Byrne's book, The Antiquities of Great Britain.

Old House with Figures
Watercolour & bodycolour on off-white paper; 262 x 390 cm;
Provenance: Lees, presented to Oldham Art Gallery, Feb 1, 1888

Old House with Figures may be a depiction of a building in the grounds of Windsor Great Park to which Sandby's brother, Thomas Sandby, had been appointed as Deputy Ranger in c.1764. Paul Sandby stayed with his brother and produced many watercolours of Windsor scenes, the first of which are dated 1863. Thomas, a self-taught artist and architectural draughtsman, also made paintings of the grounds, and the two brothers' works have often been confused. Indeed, the depiction of the building in this work compares well with some of Thomas Sandby's watercolours from the 1750's and 1760's.

Thomas Hearne

Fountains Abbey
After Thomas Hearne
Ink & watercolour on off-white paper; 285 x 260cm

This work, drawn simply in ink with watercolour washes, shows an inside view of the Abbey from the east end. It was originally thought to be one of a series of preparatory drawings that Thomas Hearne completed for *The Antiquities of Great Britain* – a topographical folio of engravings for which Hearne was responsible for supplying drawings. However, the quality of drawing in this work confirms that it is a copy, which was probably made after the finished engraving; the trees are particularly poor in relation to similar subjects in Hearne works.

The Antiquities was issued in parts from 1778 until 1786 when the project lapsed. By then, a total of fifty-two engravings had been published, which formed the first volume. In 1796 a second volume was begun with the publication of a subsequent thirty-two engravings (four per year until 1800 when Hearne's ill-health led to the prints being issued biennially) and the project was complete by 1806. In 1807 the two volumes were reissued together.

John Robert Cozens

John Robert Cozens :
1752 - 1799

Cozens is one of the greatest British watercolourists. He used few colours, often only greys and greens, yet with these conveyed a wonderful sense of mood and atmosphere. Much of his best work resulted from two trips he made to Italy – from 1776 to 1779, and 1782 to 1783. Both of the Paestum works in the Lees Collection result from the second tour. On this tour Cozens suffered a malarial illness and had to remain in Naples to recuperate. During his time there, Cozens visited local spots including Paestum. In the following years Cozens worked extensively from the sketches he made on this trip. From 1794 Cozens suffered severe mental problems and was put into Dr Thomas Munro's care. He died three years later. It was through Munro that Cozens' works became available to Turner, Girtin, DeWint and Hunt, amongst others, for copying and learning from.

Ruins of Paestum near Salerno : The Three Temples

Watercolour, pencil & ink; 255 x 364cm; Provenance: W Beckford; Beckford sale, probably lot 42, Christies April 10, 1805; Baker (?); C S Bale sale, lot 27 or 28, Christie's May 13, 1881; Agnew's sale to Lees, Nov 11, 1881

This drawing, a companion piece to *Two Great Temples at Paestum* (above, right), is based on a study from page 11 of the Hamilton Sketch Books (previously known as the Beckford Sketch Books) – entitled 'John Robert Cozens; Grand Tour Sketch Books of 1782-3 Vol.IV'. The original sketch is inscribed 'The three Temples at P(a)estum' and dated 'Nov.7'. These sketch books are now in the Whitworth Art Gallery, Manchester. The scene shows the three Doric temples from the south-west. The Temple of Neptune is in the centre with the Basilica to the right and the third temple in the distance. The finished drawing differs from the sketchbook drawing by the addition of a figure and some animals in the foreground, probably to give a sense of scale.

Two Great Temples at Paestum

Watercolour, pencil & ink; 256 x 366cm; Provenance: W Beckford; Beckford sale, lot 43, Christies April 10, 1805; Baker; C S Bale sale, lot 27 or 28, Christie's May 13, 1881; Agnew's sale to Lees, November 11, 1881

Like *Ruins of Paestum near Salerno : The Three Temples* (above, left) this work also comes from a sketch, on page 13, of the Hamilton Sketch Book, and is inscribed 'The two Great Temples'. Although this sketch is not dated, it originates from the same date as the other Paestum drawings – November 7, 1782 – as Cozens only spent one day at Paestum. This work is drawn from the opposite side shown in *The Three Temples*; here the Temple of Neptune is on the right of centre with the Basilica to the left; the Tyrrhenian Sea is depicted in the distance.

Two other watercolours on the subject of Paestum, also worked up from these sketchbooks, exist: *The Two Great Temples of Paestum*, pencil & watercolour (Victoria & Albert Museum, London); and *The Small Temple at Paestum*, watercolour (originally in the collection of Mr Peter Agnew, now Whitworth Art Gallery, Manchester).

13

Francis Nicholson

Snowdon from Capel-Curig
Pencil, watercolour & gum arabic on paper 305 x 425
Provenance: Grundy & Smith sale to Charles Lees on
December 2, 1870

As with *Landscape*, there is a rusty tone to this work, and a quite distinctive crinkled style of brushwork, especially in the painting of the group of trees in the bottom-right-hand corner.

Francis Nicholson :
1753 - 1844

Francis Nicholson was a Yorkshire painter and a founder-member of 'The Society of Painters in Watercolours' ('The Old Watercolour Society').

Landscape
Watercolour on off-white paper 230 x 347
Provenance: Fine Art Society

Most of Francis Nicholson's paintings are based in Yorkshire, although he did also work in Wales, the Lake District, Scotland, Chester, and even in Sicily.

William Payne

A Roadside Inn
Watercolour & pencil on off-white paper 420 x 552
Signed 'W Payne' (on inn sign)

This work has also been known as *A Woodside Inn*. For a long period Payne painted only Devon scenes, and only moved from Plymouth to London in 1790, to take up a teaching post. He became a popular watercolourist, known particularly for the richness and sparkle of his colours – something unusual for the time – and for his use of a bluish-grey tint (Payne's Grey) which he originated.

Edward Dayes

Chepstow Castle
Watercolour, ink & pencil on off-white paper 323 x 425
Provenance: Prob. 'Rochester Castle' lot 343, Percy sale, Christie's, April 15, 1890; Agnew's sale to Lees December 10, 1890

This castle scene was originally thought to be Rochester but is now identified as Chepstow. The accepted date of execution, 1804, is dubious, as it comes so close to the end of Dayes' life. His works are generally topographical, and drawn in Indian ink and watercolours.

William Payne :
c.1760 - c.1830

William Payne was a Devon artist who was befriended by Sir Joshua Reynolds.

Edward Dayes :
1763 - 1804

Edward Dayes was widely known as a watercolourist during his lifetime, but he also engraved and painted miniatures.

George Barret (Jnr)

William Alexander

An Old House

Pencil & watercolour on off-white paper 212 x 311cm;
Signed 'W Alexander RA' (LR)

William Alexander produced drawings for a number of
publications, and in 1808 joined the British Museum in
London, where he was in charge of prints and drawings.
The architectural detail of this work illustrates Alexander's
training and work as a draughtsman.

George Barret (Jnr) :
1767 - 1842

George Barret (Jnr) was inter-
ested in history and the clas-
sics. Many of his works have a
sentimental feel to them.

William Alexander :
1767 - 1816

William Alexander was best
known for his Oriental draw-
ings, and in particular for his
accurately drawn representa-
tions of China, where he trav-
elled in 1792.

Landscape

Watercolour, pencil, ink & gum arabic on off-white paper
224 x 325cm

In 1804 Barret was a founding member of the 'Society of
Painters in Watercolours' (the 'Old Watercolour Society'),
and his works from this period were mostly scenes in the
Thames and London vicinities. *Landscape* probably comes
from this time, although the exact location of the scene,
showing a figure trudging across a ford during a heavy
rainfall, is unknown.

Samuel Owen

Sea Piece

Watercolour on off-white paper 150 x 214   ; Signed 'S Owen' (LC)

Samuel Owen was well-known as a marine painter and this small undated work may well be a study for one of the grand battle-scene oil paintings he regularly exhibited at the Royal Academy from 1794 to 1807. The ship depicted flies the Red Ensign of the Merchant class of ships. However, it also carries a broadside of ten guns and is evidently an English Privateer. On the left in the middle distance is a Dutch brig at anchor.

Robert Hills

Turnip Field

Watercolour & bodycolour on cream paper 298 x 421   ; Signed and dated 'R.H.Hills 1819' (LR); Provenance: CJ Pooley sale, 1818

At the time of *Turnip Field* Hills was living in London having just recovered from a long illness. His recuperation had been at Farnley where he'd been able to draw and study deer. However, *Turnip Field* probably depicts an agricultural scene on the continent. Hills had made his first trip abroad in 1814, when he travelled to Paris. In 1815 he made an extensive trip to Flanders and Holland that resulted in the publication of a folio entitled *Sketches in Flanders & Holland* of 1816. The illustrations, including many of peasants and farm workers, closely resemble those of *Turnip Field* in terms of costume and pose.

Samuel Owen :
1768 - 1857

An accomplished marine painter, Owen was a member of the "Associated Artists in Watercolour" – a group that was founded in 1808.

Robert Hills :
1769 - 1844

Hills is primarily known as a painter and etcher of animals. Between 1798 and 1817, Hills produced 780 etchings of various animals as a compendium for artists. This skill led him to collaborate with other artists by painting animals into their landscapes. Many works by G F Robson (Hills' life long friend), George Barret and W A Nesfield were worked on in this way.

Henry Edridge

Lambeth
Pencil & watercolour on off-white paper 272 x 376
Provenance: Agnew's

The scene is the Thames looking towards Vauxhall; the tower of Lambeth Church can be seen (extreme left) and the old Vauxhall Bridge is in the distance. This bridge was commenced in 1811 and completed by 1816, which narrows down the date of this work to c.1816-21. (The bridge was demolished in 1898.)

Henry Edridge :
1769 - 1821
Henry Edridge was best known during his day as a painter of miniature portraits. He worked initially in black lead pencil and Indian ink, and only started using watercolour later in his career.

Coast Scene
Watercolour on off-white paper 230 x 336   ; Dated & inscribed 'Oct. 29. 1810 - Two Brothers - Gay Days - Boats & Brighton' (B)
Provenance: Fine Art Society

Until its recent restoration the subject of this work was unknown. The uncovering of the inscription on the back both dates and identifies the scene. The date, October 29, 1810, anticipates by four years an engraving *Beach at Brighton* that Edridge made for *Southern Coast (1814)*, a compendium of engraved works. It is comparable to two Constable works in the Lees collection (page 26).

18

Thomas Girtin

Egglestone Abbey
Watercolour, ink & pencil on off-white paper 390 x 445

In his watercolour drawings Girtin employed the techniques and methods taught to him by Edward Dayes until about 1795. From 1796 Girtin broke away from Dayes' methods and, as an artist, became "an interpreter rather than a recorder of the aspects of nature". *Egglestone Abbey*, which prominently shows the ruins of the Abbey's east window, dates from about 1796-98 and illustrates Girtin's mature style. Another view of Egglestone is in the British Museum. From about 1794 to 1795 Girtin occasionally toured the British Isles with James Moore, an antiquarian who produced several illustrated works listing abbeys, monasteries and castles etc. Indeed, Girtin's first work to be exhibited at the Royal Academy (1794) was a drawing, *Ely Minster*, worked up from a sketch by Moore. Later Girtin travelled with Turner.

Kirkstall Abbey
After Thomas Girtin
Watercolour & pencil on off-white paper 283 x 394
Inscribed 'Kirkstall Abbey' .

This work is a copy after the Girtin drawing, *Kirkstall Abbey, Yorkshire, Evening* (c.1800), in the V&A Museum, London. Girtin's interest was in capturing the spirit of the place and is a shift away from objective topography. Martin Hardie states:
"Cozens took a step towards simplification, but Girtin was the first to see the tree as a mass, to overcome his consciousness of its anatomy, to look at it with half-closed eyes as a dark rounded object in nature, with irregular broken contours, and to render its general tone, its lights and shadows, rather than its leaves."

Thomas Girtin :
1773 - 1802

Thomas Girtin was an extremely gifted artist who died in his twenties. Around 1796, Girtin broke away from the objective topographical style of watercolour and started to interpret rather than simply record scenes. He became interested in trying to capture the feel of a place, rather than the appearance. Girten, following in the steps of Cozens, was an important figure in making watercolour an artform in its own right, rather than a medium for sketching working studies for larger oil paintings. Such was the power of Girtin's later work that his friend, J.M.W. Turner, is supposed to have remarked: "if Girtin had lived, I should have starved".

Joseph Mallord William Turner

Joseph Mallord William Turner :
1775 - 1851

Turner was and is one of the most famous and important of all British artists. He is particularly celebrated for his move away from rigid academic forms of painting towards highly personal explorations of all the aspects and moods of nature, both in watercolour and oil. He was prolific in output, and travelled extensively throughout Britain and Continental Europe.

Blackfriars Cross, Hereford (A Monument)
Watercolour & pencil on off-white paper 250 x 173

This work is almost identical to *The Preaching Cross, Hereford* (c.1793-94) at the City Museum & Art Gallery, Stoke-on-Trent (another version of the work is at Hereford Art Gallery). A related and less finished drawing, *Cross at Entrance of Hereford,* is in the collection of the John Herron Art Museum, Indianapolis, U.S.A. Turner first visited Hereford in 1792 and again in 1793 and 1795.

A Swiss Alpine Valley (possibly St Gothard)
Watercolour & pencil on off-white (Whatman) paper 226 x 292
Provenance: Lot 48, G R Burnett sale, Christies, March 18, 1882;
E F White sale, January 21, 1887; Agnew's sale to Lees,
February 25, 1887

This work was, until recently, known as *The Rhine Above Schaffhausen.* Turner painted the falls of the Rhine at Schaffhausen on several occasions, including 1841, which was accepted as the date of this work under its old title. However, the subject is now identified as probably St Gothard and can be dated to c.1843. It can be compared with *Valley of St. Gothard* (dated c.1841) and *A View in Switzerland.* Turner's first St Gothard drawings were executed in 1802.

20

Bellinzona - The Bridge Over the Ticino
Watercolour & pencil on off-white paper 235 x 330   ; Provenance: E F White sale, January 21, 1887; Agnew's sale to Lees, February 25, 1887

Prior to 1983 this watercolour was known as *Bridge over the Moselle*. In 1980 it was pointed out that the scene depicted is not of the Moselle but of Bellinzona, north-east of Lugano, Switzerland. In 1983 a member of the Turner Society fully identified the subject: "…the measurements of the Oldham watercolour correspond almost perfectly to the size of the leaves in the sketchbook which Finberg gives as 8 x 12 so it appears that this watercolour was originally a leaf from the Bellinzona sketchbook." It is also possible that this work was amongst a series Turner made, c.1842, on the subject of Bellinzona. Ruskin noted "…a grand series of sketches made by Turner for complete pictures but never realized." The City Art Gallery, Manchester, has a work *Bellinzona No.2* which was owned, at one time, by Ruskin.

Convent at Villa Giulia, Lake Como
Attributed to Joseph Mallord William Turner

Pencil & watercolour on (Whatman) paper; 241 x 352   ; inscribed 'Convent near the Villa Julia Lago di Como, J.M. Turner R.A.' (B). Provenance: C S Bale sale, lot 171, Christie's May 13, 1881; Agnew's sale to Lees, November 11, 1881

This work is a copy after J R Cozens made at the Munro School, by Turner, Girtin or another hand.

Country Cross
Attributed to Joseph Mallord William Turner

Watercolour & pencil on off-white (Whatman) paper; 240 x 162   ; Provenance: Possibly lot 620, Broderips(?) sale, Christie's as 'A Cross in a Village' sold through Agnew's to Lees on April 2, 1872

Lucerne Near Altdorf
Attributed to Joseph Mallord William Turner

Watercolour & pencil on cream paper; 239 x 381   ; Inscribed 'Lake Lucerne / J M Turner RA CIB Lake Lucerne near Altorf. Provenance: C S Bale sale, lot 173, Christie's May 13, 1881; Agnew's sale to Lees, November 11, 1881

Like *The Convent at Villa Guilia, Lake Como* (left), this is a copy after J R Cozens, made at the Munro School by Turner, Girtin or another hand. Indeed, Cozens painted several views of Lake Lucerne late in the summer of 1776 including *Schwyz, Lake of Lucerne* which is very similar in execution and composition to this work.

Castle
Attributed to Joseph Mallord William Turner

Watercolour & pencil on off-white paper; 164 x 235   ; Provenance: Possibly A Levy sale, lot 176, Christie's June 21, 1884; Agnew's sale to Lees, December 18, 1884

The latest school of thought is that this work is almost certainly not by Turner, and that it most probably shows an imaginary castle.

John Constable

John Constable was perhaps the finest, certainly the most celebrated, of British landscape painters. He dedicated his whole career to the study of British landscape, in particular portraying the effects that different weather conditions have on the appearance of the countryside. The work of Constable from the early 19th century, along with Turner, signified the culmination of a school of British landscape painting established by notable painters such as Gainsborough and Cozens, in the previous century.

In Helmingham Park, Suffolk
Black chalk on off-white paper; 255 x 203   ; Inscribed 'In Helmingham Park, Suffolk' (B). Provenance: Lot 37, C G Constable sale, Christies, July 11, 1887; Shepherd

Constable visited the Earl of Dysart's Suffolk home in 1800 and made many sketches of Helmingham Park: some were later worked up into oil paintings. It is probable that this work remained in a sketchbook and was not one of the useful (sic) drawings referred to in the following letter that Constable wrote whilst at Helmingham Park: "Here I am quite alone amongst the Oaks and solitudes of Helmingham Park…There are abundance of fine trees of all sort… I have made one or two…drawings that may be useful."

Stoke-by-Nayland Church, Suffolk
Black chalk on buff-coloured paper 242 x 199 Inscribed 'Stoke-by-Nayland, Suffolk' (B) Provenance: A charcoal drawing, 'Stoke-by-Nayland Church' was sold at the C G Constable sale, lot 36, Christies, July 11, 1887; Shepherd

There is some question as to the subject of this drawing. In some of Constable's depictions of Stoke-by-Nayland Church the buttresses extend to the top of the parapet; in this drawing they do not. Also, Stoke-by-Nayland Church is usually shown with a clerestory whereas this work shows a simple building with raked roof.

Old Sarum

Black & white chalk on buff-coloured paper; 196 x 310   ; Inscribed & dated 'Old Sarum Sep. 14 1811' (B). Provenance: Lot 41 or 42, C G Constable sale, Christies, July 11, 1887; Shepherd

These two drawings resulted from a trip Constable made to Salisbury in 1811. *Old Sarum* is the first of many drawings Constable made of this subject and shows the mound of Old Sarum with Salisbury Cathedral in the distance.

Salisbury Cathedral from Old Sarum

Black & white chalk on buff-coloured paper; 196 x 307   ; Inscribed & dated 'NE Salisbury Sep 18 - 1811' (B). Provenance: Lot 41 or 42, C G Constable sale, Christies, July 11, 1887; Shepherd

This second work, made just four days later after *Old Sarum* (left), shows a closer view of Salisbury Cathedral and is drawn from the top of the mound.

A Lugger and Hog Boat, Brighton
Ink & pencil on off-white paper; 179 x 260
Provenance: Lot 30, C G Constable sale, Christies, July 11, 1887; Shepherd

Constable sketched Brighton Beach many times during a long stay in the town (July to October, 1824). Both these works originate from a sketchbook used intermittently by the artist between 1823 and 1824 showing numerous shipping scenes at Brighton. *A Lugger and Hog Boat, Brighton* was made on September 11th, 1824.

Brighton Beach with a Rainbow: Colliers Unloading
Watercolour & pencil on cream paper; 176 x 261   ; Provenance: Lot 32, C G Constable sale, Christies, July 11, 1887

In a letter of August 29, 1824 to a friend, Constable wrote that he preferred luggers to the fishing boats. The collier ships, though, would have been close to Constable's heart; his family had traded in coal and his father had owned such a ship. Constable had worked in the family shipping business for a short while from c.1792, and would have spent time sketching the colliers.

Water Lane, Stratford St Mary

Ink & watercolour on cream paper; 232 x 181 ; Inscribed & dated '[Aug(?) 2(?) 1831] [illegible inscription] Rhamton [illegible inscription] beginning' (B). Provenance: Lot 67, C G Constable sale, Christies, July 11, 1887; Colnagh

This is a version of a work in the V&A (with the same title) drawn on October 4, 1827. The house was once known as Old Valley Farm and appears in other works by Constable.

Cock Point, Near Folkestone

Watercolour & scratching out on off-white paper; 130 x 210 ; Provenance: Lot 64, C G Constable sale, Christies, July 11, 1887; Shepherd(?)

This watercolour drawing, originally entitled *Cock Point, near Folkston (sic), from East Weir Bay - showery effect - 1833* relates to several other drawings of the same subject. One, *Folkestone from the Beach*, is in the British Museum and is drawn from a similar, albeit nearer, standpoint. In 1880, when this work (still in the possession of the Constable family) was loaned to the South Kensington Museum, the following anecdote was related:

"Cock Point; in painting this a shower of rain came on, Capt. Constable, who was with his father exclaimed, 'Oh Papa! this will spoil your picture!' 'On the contrary', said John Constable, 'it will just give it the effect I want.' "

John Varley

John Varley :
1778-1842

John Varley's early works were little more than wash-drawings, often of a topographical style.
He rapidly developed, however, into a major painter with an interest in the romantic and atmospheric aspects of landscape.

Landscape

Watercolour & gum arabic on cream paper; 179 x 504   ; Signed & dated 'J Varley 1841' (LL). Provenance: Possibly 'Landscape' sold through Agnew's to Lees on January 25, 1870; or lot 4, James sale, Christie's May 17, 1873 as 'A Composition - Landscape' sold through Agnew's to Lees on December 22, 1874

Landscape is typical of Varley's later subjects, which were often totally imagined. His wife recalled, after his death, how her husband would "…sit down of an evening and rattle off a number of sketches, from which he would the next day select those he like best and complete them in colour".

Augustus Wall Callcott

Glengary Loch
Watercolour & bodycolour on off-white paper 215 x 457

Varley is one of the most important artists represented in the Lees Collection. *Glengarry Loch* is a typically romantic landscape, which makes use of a classical landscape composition; trees in the foreground frame the scene, whilst figures in the middle ground are set against a dramatic landscape in the distance.

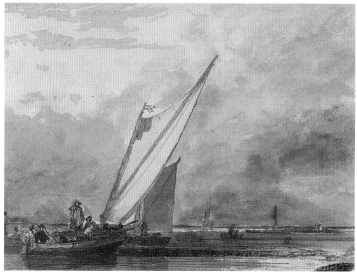

On the Medway
*Watercolour on cream paper; 261 x 345
Inscribed 'Sketch for J S (...?) ... Patron (?) of River (?) Medway' (on original mount - since removed).
Provenance: Lot 9, DeToete sale, Christie's May 8, 1885; Agnew's sale to Lees, February 25, 1887.*

Callcott painted extensively in Italy and Holland as well as in Britain. His later paintings were of classical subjects.

Augustus Wall Callcott :
1779 - 1844

Augustus Wall Callcott was a landscape painter better known for his works in oil than in watercolour. His large and bright early works are generally considered to be his best paintings.

Luke Clennell

Charles Wild

Luke Clennell :
1781 -1840

Luke Clennell was an artist particularly interested in depicting the everyday life of his time. His work includes images of smugglers, fishermen, country folk and fairground crowds.

Charles Wild :
1781 - 1835

Charles Wild was taught by Thomas Malton, the great teacher of perspective, and devoted himself almost exclusively to drawing architectural scenes.

Going to the Fair

Watercolour & pencil on off-white paper; 449 x 811
Signed & dated 'L Clennell 1812' (LR). Provenance: J Moss; Agnew's (possibly C J Pooley sale, lot 63, Capes & Dunn February 28, 1882); Agnew's sale to Lees, March 1, 1882(?)

During the period when this watercolour was painted, Luke Clennell was making contemporary life the subject of his work. Images of country folk and crowds at fairs, as in *Going to the Fair*, were common.

Crosby Hall, London I

Pencil & watercolour on paper; 342 x 294 . Provenance: Lot 71 (with 'Crosby Hall, London II') Swire sale, Christie's, February 24, 1888; Agnew's sale to Lees, December 17, 1888

On the original mounts of both *Crosby Hall, London I* (above) and *Crosby Hall, London II* (right) the following information appeared "Built in 1466. The London Palace of King Richard III". It is possible that both works were intended as illustrations to W H Pyne's *The History of the Royal Residences* for which Wild produced fifty-nine drawings, some of which were exhibited in 1818. Although they were never used they do bear comparison with several that were published. Wild's style and meticulous attention to detail was perfectly suited to this type of venture.

30

William Havell

Crosby Hall, London II

Pencil & watercolour on paper; 344 x 295   ; Provenance: Lot 71 (with 'Crosby Hall, London I') Swire sale, Christie's, February 24, 1888; Agnew's sale to Lees, December 17, 1888

The Lees family were keenly interested in Crosby Hall and Charles Lees may even have visited it when it was used as a restaurant from the late 1860's onwards. In 1923, Lees' widow, (Dame) Sarah Lees, as Vice President of the Federation of University Women, helped launch an appeal for the building to be purchased and converted into a hall of residence for women students.

Dover
Attributed to William Havell

*Watercolour & pencil on off-white paper; 450 x 620
Provenance: C J Pooley sale, 1880 (?); Grundy & Smith (?) lot 44, C J Pooley sale, Capes & Dunn, February 28, 1882; Agnew's sale to Lees, March 1, 1882*

William Havel often used touches of brilliantly bright colour to pick out details and to convey the effect of sunlight. This watercolour is similar in style to the work of Francis Nicholson.

William Havell :
1782 - 1857

William Havel travelled and painted a great deal abroad; first in China, India and Burma, and then especially in Italy. In Britain his favourite subject was the Thames region (Marlow, Windsor and Richmond), where he lived.

David Cox :
1783 - 1859

David Cox was a leading British landscape painter in both watercolours and oils (although he did not begin to paint in oils until his middle age). His drawings were rapidly executed and often display an airy and sketchy quality.

David Cox

The Terrace, Haddon
Watercolour, black chalk, & pencil on off-white paper, 211 x 284 Signed & dated 'D C 1845' (LL). Provenance: C J Pooley sale, Christies, March 6, 1880; Agnew's sale to Lees, March 20, 1883

Cox visited Derbyshire in 1831 and made the first of numerous sketches in and around Haddon Hall. In a letter to a friend and patron, written on this trip, Cox notes: "We have visited the Hall each day…Today we had Mr Severn's car and went to Chatsworth, and round by Bakewell, but did not see anything striking; but I do not expect to be much pleased with anything this country can afford after my favourite old Haddon. Indeed, that alone is quite enough for one summer."

The artist's love of Haddon is plain to see, and there can be no doubt that the terrace was a favourite subject – Cox painted many versions of it, from all angles, and occasionally with figures. *The Terrace, Haddon* is dated 1845 and must be one of very few that depict an outdoor scene – due to the atrocious weather Cox encountered that year.

Cottages
Watercolour, gum arabic, and scratching-out on paper; 212 x 310
Provenance: Agnew's sale to Lees, December 22, 1873

The subject of *Cottages* is unknown, but may well be a scene in North Wales, which Cox first visited in 1805.

Doorway at Haddon Hall
Watercolour & pencil on cream paper; 368 x 268   ; Inscribed 'Door through which Dorothy Vernon eloped' (LL to LC)

Doorway at Haddon Hall, with its dramatic inscription, "Door through which Dorothy Vernon eloped", is not dated but it is similar enough to *The Terrace, Haddon* (left), to have been made on the 1845 trip. The inscription refers to the elopement of the owner's daughter with her lover the day after her sister's wedding. The door is situated in the Long Hall used as a ballroom for the wedding festivities.

Fishing Boats

Watercolour on off-white paper; 215 x 275   ; Signed 'S Prout' (LL)
Provenance: Roberts; Agnew's sale to Lees, March 20, 1883

Samuel Prout :
1783 - 1852

Samuel Prout was very popular in Victorian times and Lees owned more works by this artist than any other.

Coast Scene

Ink, watercolour, & pencil on off-white paper; 322 x 435
Provenance: Fine Art Society (?)

At first sight this work may be a view of Dover, and is comparable to *Dover* attributed to William Havell (see p31). However, Prout, who was born in Plymouth, painted many scenes like this on the Devon and Dorset coast; similar works also depict Folkestone. Brown wash drawings are common in Prout's works of c.1815-20.

Although none of the works by Prout in this collection are dated, *Coast Scene* and *Fishing Boats* are earlier than the others in Lees' collection. Prout made his first trip abroad in 1819 and, thereafter, gradually abandoned all British subject from his works.

Rouen
Pencil & bodycolour on buff coloured paper; 409 x 267cm; Inscribed 'Rouen' (LL) with various other inscriptions Provenance: DeToete sale, lot 79, Christie's May 8, 1885; Agnew's sale to Lees, May 8, 1885

Prout first visited Rouen in 1819, and probably returned there in 1820 and 1826.

Old Street in Lisieux
Pencil & bodycolour on buff coloured paper; 391 x 252cm; Inscribed 'Lisieux' (LR) Provenance: Prob. S G Prout; W Pritchard Gordon; DeToete sale, lot 82, Christie's May 8, 1885; Agnew's sale to Lees, May 8, 1885

Ruskin wrote that this was "a hurried and fatigued drawing…I fancy he must have come on this subject at the end of a sickly-minded day". He knew that Prout suffered from migraines which laid him low once or twice every week.

The Rialto, Venice
Pencil & bodycolour on grey paper 252 x 369 Provenance: A Levy sale, lot 35, Christie's June 26, 1884; Agnew's sale to Lees, June 26, 1884

Prout made his first trip abroad in 1819, and from then on gradually stopped painting British subjects. He became particularly interested in painting architectural scenes on the Continent.

The Golden Fleece, Bruges
Pencil, watercolour & bodycolour on buff coloured paper 347 x 253 Inscribed 'Golden Fleece, Bruges' (LR) Provenance: DeToete sale, lot 78, Christie's May 8, 1885; Agnew's sale to Lees, May 8, 1885

Cathedral, Milan
Pencil & bodycolour on cream paper 276 x 423 Inscribed 'Milan' (LR) with various other inscriptions Provenance: lot 130, A Levy sale (?), Christie's June 26, 1884; Agnew's sale to Lees, June 26, 1884

Casa D'Oro, Venice
Pencil & bodycolour on blue grey paper 262 x 371 Inscribed 'Casa d'Oro' (LC) Provenance: A Levy sale, lot 133, Christie's June 26, 1884; Agnew's sale to Lees, June 26, 1884

Both these Venice works (above and near left), probably date from the 1820's. Prout first visited Venice in 1824 and then again in 1825 or 1827; on the latter trip Prout made many drawings for an unrealised publication.

Peter De Wint

Peter De Wint :
1784 - 1849

Peter De Wint ranks as one of the most important of British watercolourists. His work most certainly helped to raise the profile of watercolour painting in the first half of the 19th century. He painted almost exclusively in Britain.

Cannock Chase

Watercolour, pencil & scratching out on off-white paper
230 x 495

A scene not far from Stafford, De Wint's birthplace. Like David Cox, De Wint painted commonplace landscapes like this work, concentrating on the everyday and ordinary countryside rather than dramatic views.

Harvest Time
*Watercolour, pencil, gum arabic & scratching out on off-white paper
300 x 497 Provenance: Possibly 'Cornfield' C J Pooley sale, sold
through Agnew's to Lees on February 7, 1878*

Whilst *Harvest Time* (above) was undergoing restoration,
a rough sketch (below) was found adhered to the back of
the work, probably put there by the artist as a support for
the main drawing.

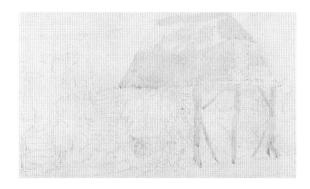

Landscape
*Watercolour & scratching out on off-white paper 299 x 469
Provenance: Fine Art Society or possibly 'A Woody Landscape' sold
through Agnew's to Lees on October 4, 1870 (?)*

This work illustrates De Wint's style of broad brushstrokes
and patches of colour (for example the bank in the lower
left corner of the painting) – a style that derives from the
work of Thomas Girtin.

Anthony Van Dyke Copley Fielding

A Moorland
Watercolour, pencil & pastel on off-white paper 333 x 460 Signed 'Copley Field...' (LC)

The scene shows a bird hunter setting off his dogs to retrieve a quarry. There is some question as to the execution of this work. The background of clouds and mountains are very different in handling to the moorland area and are quite possibly by another hand.

Anthony Van Dyke Copley Fielding :
1787 - 1855

Copley Fielding's work is generally decorative, with warm, atmospheric colours, and featuring wide sweeping views over fields, moors or sea.

Tenby
Watercolour, pencil & gum arabic on off-white paper 195 x 297 Signed & dated 'Copley Fielding 1836' (LL) Provenance: W Walton; Agnew's sale to Lees, April 19, 1883

Anthony Van-Dyke Copley Fielding's artistic reputation is based on his huge output as a painter in watercolour of both landscapes and seascapes.

George Fennell Robson

View from Fort Augustus, Caledonian Canal
*Watercolour, pencil & scratching out on off-white paper 268 x 251
Signed 'G F Robson' (LR). Inscribed 'From the Caledonian Canal at
Fort Augustus forwards Loch Ness' (B) Provenance: Lot 54, Christies
sale, June 14, 1880; Agnew's sale to Lees, November 30, 1880*

The luminosity and soft quality of light and colour in this
painting is typical of Robson's work.

Loch Coruisk, Isle of Skye
After George Fennell Robson
*Watercolour on off-white paper 241 x 329 Dated '1832' (LR)
Provenance: C J Pooley; Agnew's sale to Lees, February 7, 1878*

Between 1826 and 1832 George Fennel Robson exhibited
six Loch Coruisk scenes, of which three had quotes from
Sir Walter Scott's *Lord of the Isles* added. Scott's poem is
based on the exploits of Robert the Bruce and his followers
and in this watercolour Robert the Bruce, with two other
figures, is seen admiring the mountainous scene.
However, the rather crude technique in the painting of the
mountains and the figures, especially when contrasted to
View from Fort Augustus, Caledonian Canal (left), probably
confirms this work as a copy of the most well known version, *Loch Coruisk and the Cuchullin Mountains, Isle of
Skye* in the V&A Museum, London.

George Fennell Robson :
1788 - 1833

*George Fennell Robson came
from Durham, and although
he was based in London, his
favourite subject was the
Scottish landscape.*

William Turner of Oxford

John Martin

Landscape
Watercolour on off-white paper 240 x 323 Signed & dated 'J Martin 1839' (LR) Provenance: Agnew's

This work, showing a centrally placed pond, may be a scene at Richmond Park where Martin occasionally painted during 1839. He painted many small watercolours in areas around the river Thames and in London parks.

William Turner of Oxford :
1789 - 1862

Although Turner toured extensively in the British Isles it was his native Oxfordshire that provided the best stimulus for his work.

John Martin :
1789 - 1854

John Martin was better known as an engraver than a painter. His illustrations for the work of the poet John Milton were especially celebrated.

An Old Mill

Watercolour & scratching out on off-white paper 553 x 691 Signed & dated 'W Turner 1832' (LL). Inscribed 'The Old Windmill in Mitton Field Oxfordshire, Cuddesdon in the distance' (B)

Turner was known to give good descriptive topographical titles to his works and the inscription on the back of *An Old Mill* locates this scene exactly. This large watercolour is not unusual for Turner who produced a steady flow of finished exhibition works over his lifetime. Turner was also extremely knowledgeable of Dutch 17th century works, of which this is reminiscent, both in its subject matter and in its handling.

William Henry Hunt

An Interior
Pupil of/and William Henry Hunt
Watercolour, bodycolour & scratching out on off-white paper; 257 x 191 Provenance: J Haworth sale; Agnew's sale to Lees, April 2, 1877

Before a lengthy inscription was found on the back, this work was thought to be solely by Hunt, dating from 1839. It is now attributed to a pupil of Hunt's, possibly the sitter herself, and is earlier than thought. The sitter, said to be a Miss Moore, modelled for Hunt on several occasions. The inscription also identifies the subject of the watercolour as the housekeeper's room at Hardwick Hall.

William Andrews Nesfield

Torke Waterfall, Killarney
Watercolour, bodycolour & pencil on off-white paper 453 x 355 Provenance: Lot 181, Christie's sale, February 29, 1884; Agnew's sale to Lees, December 18, 1884

In volume II of *Modern Painters* Ruskin wrote of Nesfield's waterfall scenes: "...he has shown extraordinary feeling both for the colour and the spirituality of a great waterfall…if he would remember that in all such scenes there is much gloom as well as much splendour ... and give a little more substance to parts of his picture unaffected by spray, his work would be nearly perfect."

William Henry Hunt :
1790 - 1864

Although William Henry Hunt painted landscapes almost exclusively for the first part of his career, his later work concentrated on still-life subjects such as fruit, flowers and birds' nests. It is this later work for which he is best remembered.

William Andrews Nesfield :
1793 - 1881

William Andrews Nesfield was a watercolourist whose most admired work is set in the Scottish Highlands. He specialised in painting waterfalls. Nesfield also had a problem drawing figures; these were often contributed by artist friends.

Francis Danby was born in Ireland and came to England at age 20. A dispute with the Royal Academy, coupled with financial problems caused him to leave for the Continent in the early 1830s, not returning until the following decade. He was interested in the spiritual and poetic aspects of nature, and his paintings are often classical in appearance and highly detailed.

Francis Danby

Scene from 'A Midsummer Night's Dream'
Watercolour, bodycolour & gum arabic with scratching out on paper 199 x 281 Signed & dated (scratched out) 'F Danby 1832 (LR) Provenance: Lynell sale, lot 25, Christie's; Agnew's sale to Lees, January 29, 1875

Scene from 'A Midsummer Night's Dream' illustrates the opening of Act II, Scene 2 of Shakespeare's play and shows the meeting of Oberon and Titania which takes place in a clearing amongst tree roots. A skyline (presumably Athens) is seen top-left. In 1832 Danby was practically destitute and staying in Geneva having travelled to Switzerland to avoid mounting debt. *Scene from 'A Midsummer Night's Dream'* is one of Danby's first continental works, and its commission came through his friend George Fennel Robson (see page 41); in a letter dated 23, March 1832 to Robson, Danby writes: "…I have done as well as I could with the difficult subject which you gave me, the materials are much against it as it is more calculated for an oil picture…I most sincerely hope however that it will give some satisfaction to your friend who has done me the favour to order it…"

Landscape
Watercolour, bodycolour & pencil on off-white paper 222 x 291 Signed & dated 'F Danby 1841' Provenance: Miss Langworthy; then either Agnew's sale, November 23, 1876 or Pooley sale, February 16, 1882; Agnew's sale to Lees, March 1, 1882

The subject of this rather laboured landscape is probably imagined. Danby was living and exhibiting in London at this time and was, according to some letters he wrote that year, suffering a lack of confidence in his work. Recent opinion suggests that *Landscape* is evidence of this with its fussy and overworked attention to detail. In working out this crisis of confidence Danby created 'formula' works that relied on tried and tested technique. In these works the confidence gained in the finished product became more important than breaking new ground. Danby called these later watercolours, which are classical in appearance, "poetical landscapes".

Samuel Austin

Dort, Holland

Watercolour & bodycolour on off-white paper 344 x 509 Provenance: Lot 116, Christie's sale, June 14, 1884; Agnew's sale to Lees, December 18, 1884

Austin is known to have travelled in Holland, France and the Rhine area and *Dort, Holland* was probably painted in 1826 or 1827; although no record of a trip to Holland during this period exists, an exhibition of 1827 lists numerous Dutch scenes confirming a recent visit. Austin was noted for his paintings of Continental cities and shipping scenes.

James Duffield Harding

The Drachenfels on the Rhine

Watercolour & bodycolour on off-white paper 204 x 315

Harding's main visits to the Rhine were in 1834 and 1837. This work probably dates from the earlier trip. The Drachenfels (or 'Dragons Rock') is the highest of seven mountains on the east bank of the Rhine between Bonn and Koblenz. Harding sketched this section of the Rhine during August of 1834, with many of the drawings being published in 1838. His best works are his watercolours and his clear, precise and brightly-coloured oil paintings of the Italian Alps.

Samuel Austin :
1796 - 1834

Samuel Austin, one of the least known artists in the Lees Collection, is poorly represented in public collections.

James Duffield Harding :
1798 - 1863

James Duffield Harding was active in a number of artistic areas; as a watercolourist, oil painter, lithographer, art teacher and author of art educational publications.

James Holland

Venice
Watercolour, bodycolour & gum arabic on buff coloured paper 360 x 253 Signed & dated 'James Holland 1839' (LL) Provenance: W A Joyce (?); Gibbs; Agnew's sale to Lees, November 23, 1876

Some of Holland's scenes of Venice suffer from the garish overuse of bodycolour. Holland experimented with the addition of white to watercolour resulting in the rich colouring in *Venice*. It is said that his overuse of colour was a direct result of trying to please prosperous buyers.

Richard Parkes Bonington

Le Tréport Seen from the Direction of Eu
Watercolour, bodycolour, ink, pencil & scratching out on off-white paper 220 x 305 Signed 'R P Bonington' (LR) Provenance: Probably 'Rouen, Harvest Field' lot 283, Lee sale, Christie's, June 22, 1888; Agnew's sale to Lees, June 25, 1888

This watercolour dates from Bonington's trip to the north coast of France in 1821, and was, until 1965, originally thought to be a scene of Rouen. In the distance is a town which has now been identified as Le Tréport from an aquatint entitled *Tréport Vue prise du cite de la Ville d'Eu* by Newton Fielding published in J F d'Ostervald's *Excursions sur les cite et dans les ports de Normandie* (c.1824).

George Chambers

Coast Scene
Watercolour, pencil & bodycolour on paper 226 x 319

Coast scenes would have been second nature to George Chambers, who was born into a Whitby fishing family, and worked for many years in merchant shipping. Following the moderate success of paintings such as this, he went to London and spent seven years assisting in the painting of the great panorama of London at the Colloseum in Regents Park. Whilst this work depicts an everyday scene, Chambers is best known for his paintings of naval battles.

Samuel Palmer

The Herdsman
Watercolour, bodycolour, & gum arabic on off-white paper 544 x 758

Samuel Palmer painted many pastoral subjects from the 1840's onwards with the works made during the 1850's generally characterised by a heavier use of bodycolour. This was the result of Palmer's tendency to paint indoors under candle light giving heightened light effects. *The Herdsman*, which is bright in appearance, was painted c.1855 and shows a figure driving his cattle through countryside. The composition may possibly have provided the model for an etching Palmer commenced in 1858 known by three titles; *The Herdsman, The Weary Ploughman,* or *Tardus Bubulcus* (the latter being taken from Thomas Gray's *Elegy*). This shows a very similar scene of a figure returning home with his animals under moonlight. Although Palmer painted herdsman subjects during the 1850's, many for working up into etchings to illustrate poems by Milton, the size of this work (544 x 758cm) confirms that it is a finished exhibition watercolour in its own right.

George Chambers :
1803 - 1840

Born into a fishing family, Chambers spent a period as a ship decorator before he gained some commissions to paint ship "portraits".

Samuel Palmer :
1805 - 1881

Samuel Palmer was a mystic and visionary painter inspired by William Blake. He saw beauty in the everyday life of rural Britain, and from the 1840s onwards painted many, often dreamlike, pastoral scenes which convey deeply religious and spiritual feelings.

Charles Bentley

William Frome Smallwood

Charles Bentley :
1806 - 1854

Charles Bentley was known primarily as a painter of coastal scenes. His work is often bright in colour and tone.

William Frome Smallwood :
1806 - 1834

William Frome Smallwood originally trained as an architect and is best remembered for his fine attention to detail and perspective.

Wicklow Bay
Watercolour, bodycolour & scratching out on cream paper 578 x 800 Inscribed 'C Bentley Wicklow Bay Ireland' (B) Provenance: W H Day; Agnew's sale to Lees, December 3 or 18 (?), 1886

The scene shows a group of vessels with figures on Wicklow Bay, south of Dublin.

Rouen Cathedral
Pencil & watercolour on paper 364 x 265 Signed & dated 'W Frome Smallwood 18[24(?)] Provenance: Possibly Leech sale, lot 15, Christie's May 21, 1867 as 'Church of St. Maclou, Rouen' sold through Agnew's to Lees on November 16, 1887 (?)

William Frome Smallwood died young and this work is, therefore, quite rare. His architectural training, in its meticulous attention to detail and perspective, can be seen in this work. In the past this painting was wrongly known as *Church of St Ouen.*

Miles E. Cotman

A Calm
Watercolour & pencil on off-white paper 238 x 338 Provenance : C J Pooley; Agnew's sale to Lees, December 29, 1875

Miles E. Cotman concentrated almost exclusively on marine paintings, particularly of the waterways, coastlines and seascapes of his native Norfolk. His paintings are fine examples of their type, without ever reaching the level of skill and innovation of his contemporaries William Müller and Richard Parkes Bonington.

A Gale
Watercolour & pencil on off-white paper 237 x 325 Provenance : C J Pooley; Agnew's sale to Lees, December 29, 1875

Prior to 1981, this work was attributed to Miles' father, John Sell Cotman (1782-1842).

Miles E. Cotman :
1810 - 1858

Miles E. Cotman was the son of the more highly regarded artist John Sell Cotman, whom he succeeded as drawing master at Kings College, London.

William Müller :
1812 - 1845

William Müller travelled a great deal in his short career, painting a wide variety of subjects in both watercolour and oil; colourful and crowded street and market scenes in Egypt, mountain villages and their inhabitants in Greece, Switzerland, Italy and Asia, as well as restrained English landscapes.

Venice, Near the Arsenal

Watercolour on blue/grey paper 262 x 360 Inscribed & dated 'Pres l'Arsenal 1834' (LR) Provenance: Fine Art Society

William Müller made his first journey abroad in 1834 which culminated at Venice in September. Here he spent two months drawing parts of the city that he was able to reach by gondola. Another watercolour by William Müller on this subject, *Pres l'Arsenal*, dated Nov. 1834, is in the City Art Gallery, Bristol.

Rhodes

Pencil & watercolour on off-white paper 471 x 643 Signed & dated 'Rhodes W M March 7th 1844' (LL) Provenance: Fine Art Society (?); Colnaghi; Agnew's sale to Lees, January 13, 1882

Müller travelled to Lycia with Sir Charles Fellows in 1843, and this drawing was made on the return journey the following year. At Lycia, Müller stayed at a Franciscan Convent and planned some adventurous works; however, due to a shortage of watercolours - when he was reduced to using the simple palette as seen in this work - these ambitions were never fulfilled.

Egron Lundgren

Stapleton Mill
Watercolour, bodycolour & scratching out on paper & board 341 x 515 Provenance: S Oliver sale, lot 83, Christie's, April 18, 1887; Agnew's sale to Lees, November 16, 1887

This is one of Müller's British paintings, quite restricted in colour and tone. The broad brushstrokes are typical of his style.

The Grindstone
Watercolour on off-white paper 309 x 341

This is an odd work for the Lees Collection. Even though the artist, who originated from Sweden, worked in Britain for several years, he can hardly be recognised as a British artist. It is difficult to tell whether the subject is British.

Egron Lundgren :
1815 - 1875

Egron Lundgren was a Swedish artist who first came to Britain in 1853, then lived and worked here periodically for a number of years.

James Aumonier

John William North

James Aumonier :
1832 - 1911

James Aumonier painted landscapes in both water-colours and oils.

John William North :
1842 - 1924

During the 1890's J W North and G J Pinwell (see Visiting Day, *over) were associated with 'The Idyllist' group of illustrators.*

The Downs at Harting, Sussex

Watercolour, pencil & scratching out on off-white (Whatman) paper 635 x 915 Signed & dated 'J Aumonier 1885' (LR) Provenance: Agnew's

This is a typical rural scene by Aumonier. He concentrated on painting the Sussex landscape throughout his career.

The Quantock Hills

Watercolour on paper 447 x 283 Inscribed, signed & dated 'Quantock Hills J W North Aug 1873' (LL) Provenance: Agnew's (A watercolour drawing by J W North 'The Quarnock (sic) Hills' was exhibited at Agnew's (Liverpool) Annual Exhibition of Drawings 1886, No.16)

North moved to Somerset about 1868, where he remained for the rest of his life, and painted the lush countryside there. Using highly saturated colours he produced works of great luminescence, a quality seen in this work, which rarely contained figures.

George John Pinwell

Visiting Day
Watercolour, bodycolour & pencil on off-white paper 210 x 192 Signed 'G J P' (LL) Provenance: Agnew's (possibly lot 158, A Levy sale, Christie's, June 21, 1884 as 'District Visitor' purchased from Agnew's by Lees on November 18, 1884)

This watercolour shows the influence of Pinwell's work as an illustrator. It depicts a narrative about a household receiving visitors, and suggests characterisations in the faces of the figures and the relationships between them.

Adrian Stokes

By the Cattegut
Watercolour, bodycolour & pencil on paper 268 x 368 Signed 'Adrian Stokes' (LR) Provenance: Lees, presented to Oldham Art Gallery, November 14, 1888

This work was possibly purchased directly from the artist by Lees shortly after presenting his main gift of water-colours in July, 1888; he added it later that year probably as an example of contemporary practice. The scene – a Danish girl mending fishing nets – is very light in appearance and thoroughly modern for the time. As a member of the New English Art Club – a body set up to challenge traditional British methods of painting – Stokes was well aware of the need for progress and, as such, the inclusion of this work makes a fitting end to the Lees gift.

George John Pinwell :
1842 - 1875

George John Pinwell drew illustrations for a number of books and periodicals in addition to producing small water-colours. His paintings often have a poetic and refined feel to them.

Adrian Stokes :
1854 - 1935

Adrian Stokes was a member of the New English Art Club – an innovatory painting body.

OTHER WORKS
IN THE
CHARLES LEES
COLLECTION

This section details further works given to Oldham Art Gallery by Charles Lees and the Lees family. Six further watercolours were presented by Lees' daughter, Marjory, in 1952. These are catalogued here in detail. J.M.W. Turner's *Liber Studorium*, consisting of 71 engravings, was presented by Charles Lees in 1888. He also presented four oil paintings between 1886 and 1893. A further three oil paintings were presented by Marjory Lees in 1952, and the final three by the executors of Marjory Lees' will in 1970.

George Barret (Jnr)

1767 -1842

George Barret (Jnr) was a founding member of the Society of Painters in Watercolours (the 'Old Watercolour Society') in 1804. He was interested in history and the classics, and many of his works have a sentimental feel.

This work, dated 1835, is from George Barret's later period in which idealised subject matter is fused with a keen study of light. *The Return Home*, the perfect result of these two concerns, is an atmospheric composition owing much to the Romantic tradition. The almost garish simplicity of colouring has been achieved by using heavy and unconventional colour combinations. In a letter to a friend Barret states his liking for the light of the setting sun:

"I love to contemplate the dawn when stillness reigns on every side …I admire the effects of mid-day light, when beneath the shade of stately trees I rest secure from its dazzling blaze. Still more do I admire the saffron glow of the afternoon sun. But the twilight, the solemn, sober twilight is to me supreme; for this is the time the imagination, unfettered, takes its flight."

Thomas Collier

1840 - 1892

Thomas Collier - born in Glossop near the Derbyshire Peaks - was regarded as an expert moorland and sky painter. Woodland Landscape : Richmond Park *shows both these concerns.*

Adrian Bury has written of the work:
"One of the most remarkable and lovely water-colours in my experience is …*Woodland Landscape : Richmond Park* …I do not know how this picture was painted, and I do not think Collier himself could have told us …In so spontaneous a work the artist had no time for the slow processes of thought, even when sketching the difficult herd of deer in the centre…such a revelation could not have been achieved without years of technical, intellectual and emotional experience."

The Return Home
Watercolour, bodycolour & gum arabic on off-white paper 165 x 270
Signed & dated 'G Barret 1835' (LC) Provenance: Lot 26, (unknown) sale, Christie's, March 25, 1870; Agnew's sale to Lees, October 5, 1870; Marjory Lees

Woodland Landscape : Richmond Park
Watercolour & pencil on paper 276 x 379 Signed 'Thos Collier' (LL)
Provenance: Lot 174, T Collier sale, Christie's, March 24, 1892; Lees; Marjory Lees

The Holy City : The Mosque As Sakreh by Moonlight
Watercolour, bodycolour & pencil on off-white paper
200 x 353   ; Provenance: Lot 14, J Graham sale, Christie's, May 5, 1894 as 'Jerusalem,
Moonlight'; Agnew's sale to Lees, May 5, 1894; Marjory Lees

Shrimpers Leaving the Sea
Watercolour & pencil on off-white paper 328 x 517 Signed, dated & inscribed 'J B Pyne
1854 No.406' (LR) Inscribed 'Crickeith Castle, N Wales. Shrimpers Leaving the Sea' (B)
Provenance: Lees; Marjory Lees

William Holman Hunt

1827 - 1910

William Holman Hunt was a founder member of the Pre-Raphaelite Brotherhood, with Rossetti and several others, in 1848. The Brotherhood was formed in reaction to the stale traditions of academic painting based on the worship of the art of Raphael. Although the Brotherhood did not last long as a formal group, what is now thought of as the Pre-Raphaelite movement was certainly the most significant development in 19th-century British art. Pre-Raphaelite painting was marked by an intense observation of nature, represented in fine detail, and a deeply spiritual and religious outlook. Hunt travelled extensively through the Holy Lands, living in Jerusalem for over a year. This experience deepened his religious convictions and led him to paint extremely detailed biblical scenes in his later life.

In January 1854 Hunt left England to join Thomas Seddon, a fellow artist, in Egypt and the two men travelled to Jerusalem together arriving in June 1854. Hunt stayed in a missionary's house for over a year where he had an excellent view of Jerusalem.   Hunt wrote about the scene depicted in this work as follows: "One evening, when settled in my new home, as the moon was shining splendidly, I raised myself to look over the high wall on my roof, and stood gazing on the impressive view of the Mosque of El Aksa, the swaying dark cypresses; the arcades and eastern wall stood backgrounded by the Mount of Olives. It was a poetic and absorbing scene ... the moonlight effect enchanted me." This was the last watercolour work Charles Lees purchased from Agnew's, possibly the last before his death.

James Baker Pyne

1800 - 1870

James Baker Pyne was a watercolourist interested in both landscape and figure painting. His works generally show a very decorative use of colour.

Shrimpers Leaving the Sea was originally thought to be a scene of Lancaster Sands; this erroneous information was supplied by Marjory Lees after seeing a similar work by Pyne, in oil, at the Russell Cotes Art Gallery, Bournemouth in 1936. The inscription on the back, discovered during the recent restoration of the work, identifies the subject.

Dante Gabriel Rossetti

1828 - 1882

Dante Gabriel Rossetti was one of the most important artists of his day. Along with William Holman Hunt he founded the Pre-Raphaelite Brotherhood in 1848. He was a close associate of William Morris, Ford Maddox Brown and Edward Burne-Jones, with whom he instigated the Arts and Crafts Movement in the 1860s and 1870s

This work is one of the last medieval subjects that Rossetti completed. Although the scene depicted is from Hamlet (Act IV Sc.5) there has been confusion regarding the exact passage Rossetti has illustrated. According to the text, in the middle of the scene Ophelia is led away by Horatio after the King and Queen discover her madness. This accords with an earlier title for the work *The First Discovery of Ophelia's Madness*, but, towards the end of the scene Ophelia reappears adorned with straws and flowers clearly suggested by Rossetti in Ophelia's dress. If the work shows the earlier passage then the figure on the left should be Horatio (as in the work's present title); if the latter, then the figure represents Laertes, her brother. In both cases the two figures on the right are the King and Queen. Further confusion is added by the fact that, according to the artist's family, Rossetti introduced the character of Horatio into a scene which does not take place in the play. The result is that the scene represents the latter appearance of Ophelia but with Horatio in place of Laertes. Rossetti contrived such inventions to create a scene symbolic of character and situation.

Horatio Discovering the Madness of Ophelia

Watercolour, bodycolour & pencil on off-white paper 409 x 307 Signed & dated 'D G R (in monogram) April 1864' (LL) Provenance: W Dunlop; lot 108, W Graham sale, Christie's April 3, 1886; H Roberts sale, Christie's, February 2, 1891; Agnew's sale to Lees, March 25, 1892; Marjory Lees

John Ruskin

1819 - 1900

Ruskin was the most important art writer and critic in 19th-century Britain. He published some 80 works, including his five volume Modern Painters. *He illustrated many of his own works, including his famous three volume work on architecture,* The Stones of Venice. *Ruskin was also a very public supporter of the Pre-Raphaelites.*

John Ruskin made numerous trips to Venice and became seriously interested in its architecture from 1845. Many sketches showing fragments of Venetian buildings date from this time. It is probable that this sketch, showing part of an archivolt on the outer entrance of St Mark's, was drawn as a study for *The Stones of Venice* which Ruskin commenced in 1849 and was published in 1853. This drawing was not included in *The Stones of Venice* but descriptions of the twelve month archivolts are – the drawing may have been an *aide-memoire*. Ruskin states that the archivolts are Gothic in feel and, as such, depart from the generally Byzantine architecture of St Mark's – they may well have been a later addition. *The Stones of Venice* shows a wood carrier flanked by two birds (possibly peacocks in a Byzantine style). The wood carrier is a rare symbol for January; he is often represented as a two-headed Janus, or an old man. This work was originally given to Oldham Art Gallery on long-term loan around 1936. In 1952 Marjory Lees presented it with five other watercolours.

First of the Months Sculpture - St Mark's, Venice
Pencil & watercolour on off-white card 222 x 154   ; Inscribed 'January - 1st of the Months on the Archivolt of St Mark's' [B] Provenance: Agnew's(?); Lees; Marjory Lees.

Frontispiece: 188 x 265
Published May 23, 1812 & issued with Part X; Engraved by J C Easling (centre by J M W Turner)
The central panel shows 'The Rape of Europa' by Titian.

The *Liber Studiorum* (Book of Studies) was presented to Oldham Art Gallery by Lees on July 25, 1888 with the main gift of water-colour drawings. Lees probably purchased the *Liber Studiorum* as a complete or near complete set from Agnew's. Many sets and individual engravings had been dispersed in 1873 when, twenty-two years after the artist's death, the personal properties and works of Turner were sold through Christie's (Turner's will had been the subject of a long case of litigation). Agnew's purchased heavily from this sale and probably sold a set on to Lees.

The *Liber Studiorum* was commenced by Turner after a friend suggested it as a way of securing future fame. It was conceived as a schematic series of engravings and, in this respect, departed from the *Liber Veritatis* of Claude, to which it is often compared. The *Liber Veritatis* was initially a set of drawings made for the sole purpose of identifying Claude's own paintings and never intended for publication. After Claude's death the drawings were engraved, with the engraver taking the liberty of changing the original designs to make them suitable for engraving. In contrast, the designs for the *Liber Studiorum* (worked up from new or existing drawings) were all etched in the early stages by Turner. After he had etched the copper plates, giving a line of representation, they were engraved by professional engravers giving areas of light and dark. This gave

Ships in a breeze: 181 x 258

Turner a great deal of control over the finished image. The *Liber Studiorum* was arranged into six classification groups; Pastoral, Elegant Pastoral, Marine, Mountainous, Architecture and Historical. This categorisation of the engravings was a means by which Turner could show-off the range of his work.

From about 1820-23 Turner began to lose interest in the venture and decided to abandon the project. This decision, hastened by its lack of commercial success, rested on many factors. There is no doubt that his fame had spread, thus fulfilling one of his original intentions, and, consequently, he was busier than ever with painting; but the engraving skills he'd learnt aided him in his other work. At the time of abandonment at least eight of the outstanding twenty-nine had been worked on by Turner and another three may have been. Indeed, many of these were already in plate form. The rest are questionable and may be attributed to other engravers. After the 1873 sale some of the original copper plates for the unfinished engravings were discovered and during the 1880's Frank Short, a leading engraver of the time, experimented by making prints from these. This led to the publication, in 1897, of seventeen of the outstanding works. Oldham Art Gallery added fourteen of these to Lees' *Liber Studiorum* in 1898. This 'completed' as far as possible the *Liber Studiorum* of Turner.

61

OIL PAINTINGS

ANNIE SWYNNERTON : 1844 - 1933

Cupid and Psyche

Oil on Canvas

1494 x 925

Signed & dated 'Annie Swynnerton 1890' (LR)

Provenance: Artist; Lees; presented October 26, 1892

Oldham Art Gallery was keen to exhibit this work in the annual Spring Exhibition of 1892. However, it had already been sold to Lees who had promised it to the Autumn Exhibition in Liverpool. Oldham's interest in the work may have been the impetus for Lees' presentation later the same year. In a letter to Lees shortly after the purchase, Annie Swynnerton wrote:

"In these days when English Art is almost altogether discouraged for French and Anglo-French Art it is indeed no small gratification to find that some few have sufficient patriotism to remain faithful to their countrymen. Art to be of any value must be native born..."

GEORGE CLAUSEN : 1852 - 1944

Phyllis

Oil on canvas

622 x 312

Signed & dated 'G Clausen 1880' (LL)

Provenance: McLean sale, October 13, 1880; Agnew's sale, March 29, 1881; Lees; Marjory Lees; presented 1952

GEORGE AIKMAN : 1830 - 1905

Weighing the Anchor

Oil on Canvas

609 x 1018

Signed 'G Aikman' (LL) & dated '1880' (LR)

Provenance: Lees; presented December 20, 1893

Aikman was a regular lender to Oldham Art Gallery and *Weighing the Anchor* was exhibited at the Oldham Spring Exhibition of 1892 where it was purchased by Charles Lees. The following year he presented it to the Art Gallery.

DAVID MURRAY : 1849 - 1934

Twixt, Croft and Creel

Oil on Canvas

1020 x 1521

Signed & dated 'D Murray (18)85' (LL)

Provenance: Artist; Lees; presented January 13, 1886

This work was painted at Tarbert, Loch Fyne and shows a group of crofters working. Lees purchased it from the Manchester Art Exhibition of 1885 with the intention of presenting it to Oldham Art Gallery. A local paper reported at the time that the work was given "...toward the formation of a permanent gallery of pictures".

IGNACE HENRI JEAN THEODORE FANTIN-LATOUR : 1836 - 1904

Roses II

Oil on canvas

405 x 328

Provenance: Lees (probably purchased from the Oldham Spring Exhibition of 1883 where it was exhibited as no.83); Marjory Lees; presented 1952

ALFRED PARSONS : 1847 - 1920

Meadows by the Avon

Oil on Canvas

950 x 1510

Signed & dated 'Alfred Parsons 1884' (LR)

Provenance: Prob. artist; Lees; presented January 13, 1886

GEORGE FREDERICK WATTS: 1817 - 1904

Aurora (c.1842)

Oil on arch-shaped canvas

864 (at highest point) x 919

Provenance: A A Ionides sale, January 13, 1894; Agnew's sale, June 29, 1894; Lees; Marjory Lees; bequeathed 1970

JOHN WILLIAM WATERHOUSE : 1849 - 1917

Circé Offering the Cup to Ulysses

Oil on canvas

1464 x 902

Signed & dated 'J W Waterhouse 1891' (LL)

Provenance: The artist; Lees; Marjory Lees; presented 1952

Lees purchased this work directly from the artist possibly through the Oldham Spring Exhibition of 1892 (cat. no.70) and immediately prevented his new acquisition from going to an exhibition in Munich. Whilst in London, Lees tried to visit Waterhouse at his Primrose Hill studio (where the work was painted) to find out more about the picture. The artist was out but, later, wrote a lengthy letter to Lees about the painting.

The work illustrates the meeting of Ulysses with Circé as told by Homer. In the letter, dated July 20, 1891, Waterhouse erroneously gives the reference in Andrew Lacy's translation as Book XI of *The Odyssey* (the story of this particular event is recounted in Book X). *Circé* is said to be the first of Waterhouse's Homeric subjects and it shows the emergence of the artist's distinctive Classical style. It was one of just two major works Waterhouse completed in 1891.

A study for *Circé Offering the Cup to Ulysses* is in the Waterhouse sketchbooks at the Victoria and Albert Museum. Another work, *Circé Invidiosa* (in the Art Gallery of South Australia, Adelaide) illustrates a scene from later in *The Odyssey*.

JOHN EVERETT MILLAIS : 1829 - 1896

The Departure of the Crusaders (1857-8)

Oil on canvas

530 x 661

Signed in monogram (LL)

Provenance: Gambart, 1861; Caine sale, May 6, 1871; Agnew's sale, October 6, 1871; K Finlay sale, February 19, 1891; Agnew's sale to Lees, March 9, 1892; Marjory Lees; bequeathed 1970

This work, a sketch intended for a larger work entitled *The Crusaders Return*, was commenced by Millais during 1857 after discussions with Holman Hunt. After working on it through the winter of 1857-8 he abandoned the whole project in the spring and was never to return to it. It was later sold to the London dealer Gambart in 1861.

JOHN PETTIE: 1839 - 1893

Portrait of Charles E. Lees

Oil on canvas

1498 x 1257

Signed 'Pettie' (LR)

Provenance: Lees (presumably commissioned); Marjory Lees; bequeathed 1970

JOHN PETTIE - *Portrait of Charles Lees (detail)*
This portrait was painted in 1884 and shows Lees aged 44.